Visit https://bit.ly/weaningguide
to access a free gentle weaning guidebook
with weaning tips and a gentle night weaning plan.

Please email author@jessicaelder.com if you have
any problems accessing the link!

Dedication

For my babies...thank you for the beautiful
memories.

J.E.

My Milk Will Go, Our Love Will Grow
Text copyright ©2019 Jessica Elder
Illustration copyright ©2019 Sheila Fein
All rights reserved. Printed in the United States of America.

W
Heart Words Press™

Book Design, Illustration, and Layout by Sheila Fein

ISBN # 9781733417716

My Milk Will Go, Our Love Will Grow

A Book for Weaning

By Jessica Elder

Illustrated by Sheila Fein

My baby, look at you!
You're growing more each day.
My heart is filled with pride.
I have a lot to say.

When you were really small,
my milk helped you to grow.

But now you need to know
my milk is almost gone.
My body can't make more,
but love for you goes on.

But, Mom, I still want milk.
Your milk will go away?

I know it's
hard to hear.
Have questions?
It's okay.

I see you thinking hard,
How will my day go now?
A lot will stay the same.
Please let me show
you how.

With milk and food to eat?

For milk you'll need a cup.
For meals you'll use a seat.

And when I'm sick or hurt?

You still can count on me.
I'll help to ease the pain.
Bring comfort, you will see.

And if I'm scared or sad?

Then I will hold you tight.
I'll look into your eyes,
and things will be all right.

And when it's time for bed?

We'll read and sing a song.
You'll cuddle close to me,
right here where you belong.

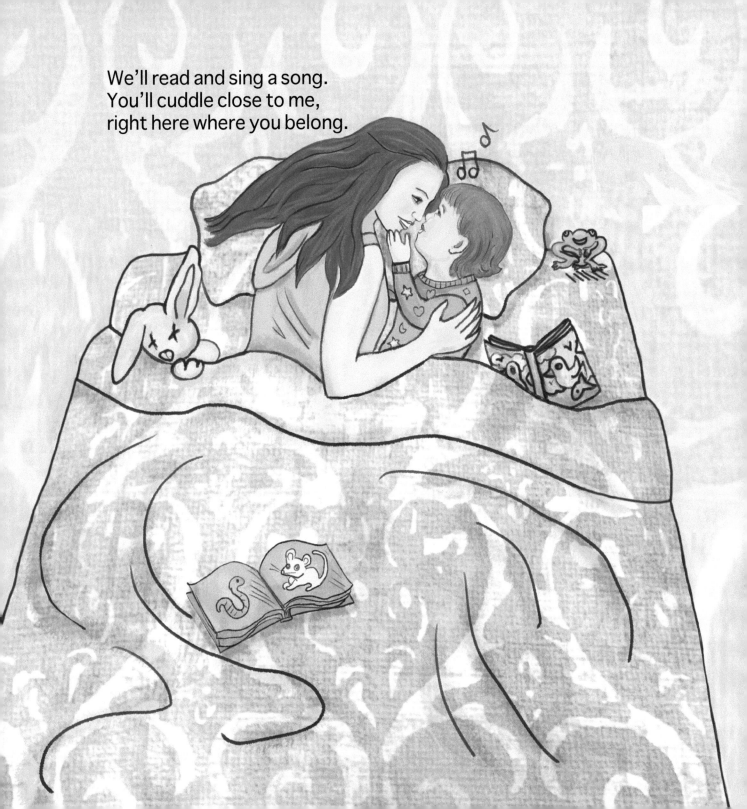

If I wake up for milk?

Just call, I'll come to you.
I won't have milk to give.
I think a hug will do.

I love my mama's milk.
I feel a little sad.

I'm also feeling sad.
I'm sorry for this change.
Together we'll go on,
and soon it won't
feel strange.

I'm glad we've had this time.
It's true, my milk will go.
But, dear, you are so loved.
Each day our love will grow.

About the Author

Jessica Elder, a writer and social worker, has extensive training in infant and child mental health, child development, and parent-child relationships. Jessica's writing is inspired by her own parenting experiences and by years of professional experience supporting children and families through life challenges and transitions. Jessica breastfed her babies and weaned them when they were toddlers. While nursing her second newborn in 2016, she was inspired to write *My Milk Will Go, Our Love Will Grow*, hoping it would help toddlers acknowledge their feelings around weaning and understand that their needs will still be met. Jessica grew up in the suburbs of Pittsburgh, Pennsylvania, where she earned a bachelor's degree in psychology at the University of Pittsburgh. She met her future husband while in college. Jessica earned a master's degree in social work at Columbia University and received postgraduate training at the Institute for Psychoanalytic Training and Research. She developed her career in New York City as a clinical social worker and program developer. Jessica now lives in Arizona with her husband, children, and rescue dog. She continues to practice social work and also enjoys writing. She is a member of the Society of Children's Book Writers and Illustrators (SCBWI).

Please visit www.jessicaelder.com for more information.

About the Illustrator

Sheila Fein is an illustrator and a fine artist. She enjoys combining the two disciplines to illustrate children's books. Raising four daughters of her own, two of which were twins, Sheila breastfed each one and was thrilled that Jessica chose her to illustrate her book on weaning. Sheila grew up on Long Island and earned her bachelor's degree in graphic design and fine art at Buffalo State College. When she is not painting or illustrating, she runs drawing workshops called Imaginings Sketch/People Sketchers for artists to study the human figure. She also teaches privately, helping others to express their own style and release their imaginations. Sheila lives in the Santa Monica Mountains of California with her husband and their chocolate lab, Charlie Sage. Her home is always open to her children, their families, friends, and other artists. Sheila is a young "Gami" with three grandchildren, two boys and one girl. She enjoys having shows of her work and is always creating something. Sheila is a PAL (published and listed) member of the Society of Children's Book Writers and Illustrators (SCBWI).

Please visit www.sheilafein.com to see her fine art work.
You can visit www.freelanced.com/sheilafein to view her illustration work.

Tips for Using this Book

Please visit https://bit.ly/weaningguide to sign up for a free gentle weaning guide and step-by-step night weaning plan to use with my book.

This book was written to help you communicate with your child about weaning, to help your child acknowledge thoughts and feelings, and to reassure your child that love will be provided and needs will be met when nursing ends. Even the youngest toddlers are capable of understanding much more than they can express with language. They can benefit from direct, honest communication, even if they do not talk in sentences or use many words.

Remember that this book can help your toddler at any point in the process of weaning. It might also help recently weaned toddlers, and weaned toddlers with a sibling who is nursing. It can be a sweet book to read to all children who have been nursed, helping them understand the nurturing you provided during their earliest years.

A lot more can be said about weaning depending on the situation, the child's age, and your child's response. You can extend the conversation about weaning in your own words and by following these tips:

• It may help to point to the mother in the story when she is talking and to point to the child when he is talking.

• In addition to reading the book, you can also point to the pictures and give simple explanations of what mom and toddler are doing and feeling. For example, "The child is wondering how his mother will help him fall asleep at night. Mama will read him books, sing songs, and cuddle. She will still be there with him." You can personalize your explanations to match your situation.

• After you read the story, you can review it in your own words and make connections. For example, "The child is worried about how his mother will comfort him, and how things will change when her milk goes away. Just like the mother in the book, I'm going to give you hugs, hold you, and will always love you."

• Sometimes toddlers may resist a book about something that makes them anxious. If this happens, try leaving the book out somewhere where the toddler can explore it. You can also try introducing the book by pointing to a picture that might catch his interest and talking about it.

You are welcome to contact me with questions through www.jessicaelder.com

Printed in the USA
CPSIA information can be obtained
at www.ICGtesting.com
LVHW060759270224
772932LV00002B/36